CW00530306

Text Copyright © Vicky Wright 2022

Illustrations Copyright © Beth Twentyman 2022

Written by Vicky Wright
Illustrated by Beth Twentyman
Edited by Helen Lewis

ISBN   978-1-3999-2491-7

We all know plants need:

- Water

- Nutrients

- Sunlight

But plants hold a number of other secrets too……

Want to be a Plant Whisperer?

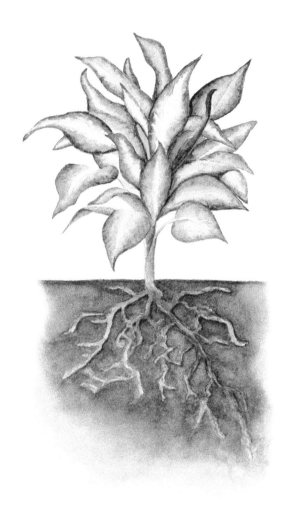

Secret 1:
Where it sits

Where you put a
plant in relation
to the sun.....

Secret 2:

The space between plants

… and where you put it in relation to other plants.

How close is it to other plants?

All plants need an invisible
space bubble, especially if
they are in a phase of growth.

Secret 3:

Plant combinations

Some plants like being next to each other.....

… and some get overcrowded.

Secret 4:

Patterns in nature

To begin discovering the best combinations, try out different groupings of plants in your home and see how they respond after a week.

Some plants will thrive next to each other, whilst others may wilt.

To learn more about plant combinations keep an eye out for self-seeding plants in your local park or garden….

When you see a self-seeding plant, look at which plants or trees are nearby and how far they are away.

By observing the pattern in nature, you will begin to see the optimal symbiotic relationships between plants.

TRICK

If you have two plants of the same species and one is struggling....

....place it next to the healthy plant and keep a look out for the changes over 2 - 4 weeks.

Secret 5:

Support from the mother plant

When a plant self-seeds and a baby plant is created, re-potting the baby plant is the next step.

To ensure strong growth and survival of the new plant, place it next to the mother plant for 5 - 7 days.

Newly potted plants kept next to their mother plant for a week have higher rates of survival.

When propagating, this placement of the mother plant can keep a new plant alive for over 8 months even when no root forms in the new plant.

Secret 6:

The "heat" of plants

Step 1: Discover the heat of your hands

- Close your eyes

- Slowly bring your hands (palm to palm) closer

At what distance can you feel the heat of the other hand?

Step 2: Discover the "heat" of a plant

- Close your eyes again

- Before physically touching the plant, bring the palm of your hand towards the plant.

At what distance do you begin to feel the "heat" of the plant?

You may find the distances vary for different plants and trees.

If you are pruning or cutting the branches of a plant.....

.... you may be able to feel the heat of the cut branch or stem on the plant immediately after.

Sometimes people can feel it 5 minutes, 20 minutes or a number of hours afterwards.

Secret 7:

Getting to know plant response times

All plants need different levels of water, nutrients and sunlight.

As we learn about and look after plants, we begin to discover if they need a lot or a little water.

For plants that need a lot of water, you may be able to see when they get thirsty…

If they are very thirsty, they will physically dry and shrivel. But if they are a little thirsty, they may appear smaller, duller and less plump.

Adding water to these plants, you may see in real-time their recovery and brightness return.

How quickly do you see a change in your favourite plants?

1 min

5 mins

2 mins

1 hour

20 mins

Secret 8 :

Knowing their origins

Each species has its unique balance of water, nutrients, sunlight and space.

For orchids adapted to live and wrap around the surface of trees in the jungle, they absorb sunlight through their green roots.

They live on very little water and nutrients, and can exist for some periods of time on sunlight and air alone.

Sunlight is an essential ingredient for photosynthesis, so in some ways, all plants are made of light!

For healthy orchid growth at home, similar to their jungle origin, they don't need much water and soil, and it's important for the roots to access sunlight, either in a glass or clear plastic pot, or by growing their roots above ground.

Secret 9:
Part of a bigger whole

Beneath a plant's life are the cycles of the seasons and natural rhythms of the world around.

Your plant may be happy and healthy, but waiting for its time to celebrate and grow new flowers, to a special underlying timing.

Orchids, for example, only create new flower stems twice a year.

Look out for plants of the same species in parks, gardens or other houses, and when they begin to flower…

You may see that your flowering house plant is joining in a far greater celebration!

Author - Vicky Wright is a natural scientist and inter-disciplinary artist, based in Kent, UK. She interweaves knowledge from ecology, therapy and physical theatre in studying the natural world.

Illustrator - Beth Twentyman is a watercolour artist, theatre mask-maker, theatre teacher and speech pathologist based in Melbourne, Australia, with a passion for studying the dynamics of how things move and how they communicate.

Vicky and Beth met when training in physical theatre in Italy, here they learnt about the concepts of spatial relationship, which prompted the discoveries to inspire this book.

 Discover the science behind this book…

Lightning Source UK Ltd.
Milton Keynes UK
UKHW020744160223
417109UK00012B/328